It was Friday afternoon at Woodside School.

All the children were about to go home.

'Who is going to take the hamster home this weekend?' said Miss Owen.

One of the children went to the cage but the hamster was not there!

'We must find the hamster,' said Miss Owen.
First of all they looked in the home corner.
The children looked under the table and
in the pots and pans.
Miss Owen looked behind the cooker but
she could not see the hamster.
She said to the children,

Can you see it?

Next Miss Owen and the children looked in the play corner.
The children looked inside the dressing up box.
Miss Owen looked in the shop but
she could not see the hamster.
She said to the children,

Can you see it?
Shop

Next Miss Owen and the children looked in the book corner.
The children looked on the shelves and in the book boxes.
Miss Owen looked under the cushions but she could not see the hamster.
She said to the children,

Can you see it?
Castles
PetCare
Hide and Seek

‘Where is that hamster?’ said Miss Owen.

All the children laughed and said,